OXFORD BOOKWORMS LIBRARY
True Stories

Hachiko
Japan's Most Faithful Dog

Stage 1 (400 headwords)

T0364654

Retold by Nicole Irving
Illustrated by Gen/Illustration Web

Series Editor: Rachel Bladon
Founder Editors: Jennifer Bassett
and Tricia Hedge

OXFORD

UNIVERSITY PRESS

Great Clarendon Street, Oxford, OX2 6DP, United Kingdom

Oxford University Press is a department of the University of Oxford.
It furthers the University's objective of excellence in research, scholarship,
and education by publishing worldwide. Oxford is a registered trade
mark of Oxford University Press in the UK and in certain other countries

ISBN: 978 0 19 402267 5
A complete recording of this Bookworms edition of
Hachiko: Japan's Most Faithful Dog is available.

Printed in China

Word count (main text): 4,724

For more information on the Oxford Bookworms Library,
visit www.oup.com/elt/gradedreaders

ACKNOWLEDGEMENTS

Cover Images: Bridgeman Art Library Ltd; (Japan: 'Faithful dog Hachiko' being fed by a Japanese
couple at Shibuya station, Tokyo, in a photograph taken 15 April, 1934, a year before Hachiko's
death/Pictures from History), Getty Images; (cherry blossoms/Hiroki – rush of happiness).

The publisher would like to thank the following for their permission to reproduce photographs:
123RF pp.41 (Greyfriars Bobby/alicephoto), 57 (Akita dog/Radomír Režný), 58 (Australian
cattle dog/bonzami emmanuelle); Bridgeman Art Library Ltd p.3 (Japan: Chuken Hachiko
'Faithful dog Hachiko' at Shibuya Station c. 1932/Pictures from History); Getty Images
pp.37 (Statue of Hachiko/Laurie Noble), 37 (Statue of 'Hachi'/The Asahi Shimbun); Oxford
Bookworms Covers pp.59 (The Elephant Man, Tim Vicary), (Red Dog, Louis de Bernières); Rex
Shutterstock pp.36 (Hachi - A Dog's Tale/Inferno/Grand Army/Scion), 36 (Hachi – A Dog's Tale/
Inferno/Grand Army/Scion).

Illustrations by: Gen/Illustrationweb (story artwork); Richard Ponsford p.iv (map of Japan)

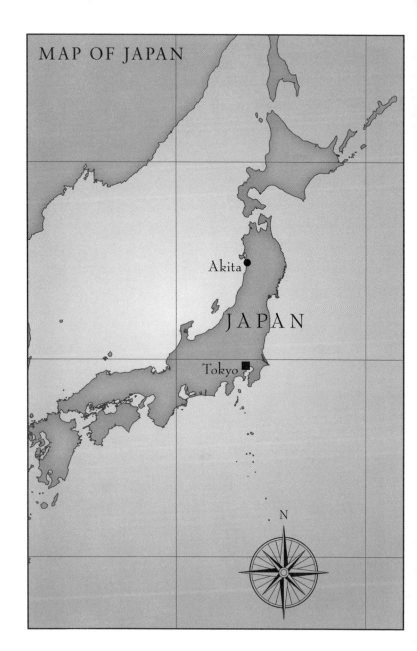

MAP OF JAPAN

Akita

JAPAN

Tokyo

N

CONTENTS

CHAPTER ONE
Puppy Days

"Come and see," the farmer called to his family. "There are eight puppies, and they're all well." His children quickly found their shoes and warm coats, and went out with him. How exciting! They ran through the cold yard to the little shed behind the house.

It was a winter night when the eight little dogs were born, and because the farmer's home was in Akita, in the north of Japan, there was a lot of snow. But the puppies were warm in the shed, next to their mother.

The farmer put his hand on the mother dog's beautiful yellow-white coat.

"You did well," he said. "You must sleep now."

The children watched their father, and they smiled. Akita was famous for these big dogs, and their father loved them.

Soon, the farmer's wife came and looked, too. "They're beautiful puppies," she smiled.

"Yes," the farmer said. "My friend in Tokyo, Professor Ueno, is going to be happy. He's waiting for a nice Akita puppy, and he's going to pay us thirty *yen*. He can have the best one."

"Oh, yes," his wife said. "Professor Ueno must have the best puppy for his thirty *yen*." She smiled at the children. "Now come and eat. Dinner's ready."

The puppies were warm in the shed, next to their mother.

For the next two weeks, the puppies drank their mother's milk and slept. Then they began opening their eyes, and they wanted to chew everything. They chewed their mother's ears and coat, and they chewed their bed, too!

After one more week, the puppies began to walk. Everyone laughed when they watched the little dogs, because they could not walk well. Then, two or three weeks later, when the puppies were bigger and could walk better, they began to play. They played a lot, and the children loved playing with them.

The puppies began to walk.

Once, when the puppies were about six weeks old, three of them began playing by the shed door. When the farmer came in with food and water for the mother dog, the three puppies ran through the open door into the yard. The farmer did not see them, and they began to play in the snow. They played and played, but soon they were very cold. There was snow on their coats and on their paws, and the puppies got colder and colder. Soon, they could not move.

In the house, the family heard the mother dog. She never usually made a noise, but now she barked and barked from her bed. The children ran out to the shed.

"Why are you barking?" the little girl asked.

Then her brother looked at the puppies and said, "Where are all your puppies? There are only five here!"

"Why are you barking?" the little girl asked.

The children went into the yard, and soon they found the three puppies in the snow. They called to their father.

"Oh, dear," the farmer said when he saw the cold little dogs. "Bring them into the house quickly. It's warm in there."

The children brought the puppies into the house. Two of the little dogs sat and cried. But one of them was interested in everything, and he did not sit down or cry.

"Look at this puppy!" said the farmer. "He's braver than his brother and sister! He's a very nice Akita dog – let's give him to Professor Ueno."

"He's a very nice Akita dog – let's give him to Professor Ueno."

❖

Soon, the puppies were bigger, and they needed to leave their mother and go to their new homes. So one day, the farmer went to the train station with the professor's puppy in a box, and spoke to the driver of the Tokyo train.

"My friend Professor Ueno lives in Tokyo," he said, "and this puppy is for him. The professor is going to meet the train at Shibuya Station."

The driver carefully took the box and put it in the train. At first, the little puppy cried, but the driver opened the box, put his hand on the dog's head and said, "It's OK, little puppy. You're going to your new home." Then the dog slept.

After many hours, the train arrived at Shibuya Station in Tokyo, near the professor's house.

"Thank you," said Professor Ueno when he took the box from the train driver. He looked at the dog's yellow-white face and dark eyes. "Oh, he's beautiful," the professor smiled.

"Yes, he is," said the train driver. "You've got a nice dog there, Professor."

CHAPTER TWO

A New Home

I was only five years old when I first met Hachiko.
Professor Ueno often came after work and drank green
tea at my parents' *yakitori* stall near the station. So
when he left the station with his new puppy that day in
1923, he stopped and said hello to my parents and me.
My parents often took me to the stall with them, so I
knew Professor Ueno, and I liked him.

I remember that day well. The professor put the box
on a stool and said to me, "Have a look, Nobu."

I looked into the box.

"It's a puppy!" I cried.

The professor took the dog out of the box, and I put
my hand on its warm coat.

"What a beautiful dog, Professor!" my mother said.

Professor Ueno smiled. "Yes – and he's brave, too, I
think. There are a lot of different noises here in Tokyo,
but he isn't afraid." The professor put the little dog back
in its box. "I'm going to take him back to my house now,
but we can come and see you again soon, Nobu."

The professor carried his new dog home, and when
they arrived in the professor's yard, the puppy slowly,
carefully came out of his box. He was afraid at first. But
he was hungry and thirsty, so soon he ate some rice with
fish, and drank some water.

"It's a puppy!"

Then he began playing, and the professor watched him. The puppy was quick and strong. He ran and looked in the yard, and wanted to play with everything. When the little dog got tired, the professor sat on a chair with him, and the puppy soon went to sleep. So when Mrs. Ueno came home from the shops that day, she walked into the yard and found her husband with the puppy in his arms.

They gave the little dog the name Hachiko.

"Meet our little Akita puppy," her husband said.

The dog opened his dark eyes and wagged his tail happily.

"Hello!" said Mrs. Ueno, and she smiled at the puppy's little face. "Oh, you are beautiful. We're going to love you!"

"What are we going to call him?" the professor said to his wife.

They gave the little dog the name Hachiko. *Hachi* means eight in Japanese, and the dog's mother had eight puppies. In Japan, eight is a good number, too.

The professor made a warm bed for the puppy in a yard shed near the house, and Hachiko slept quietly there that night.

Professor Ueno worked at the University of Tokyo, and the next day, when he went to work, Hachiko stayed at home in the yard. He played there happily. Then he found a shoe near the front door of the house, and he took it to his bed and chewed it.

"Stop, and give me that shoe," Mrs. Ueno said when she came into the yard. "You bad dog! That's one of the professor's shoes! He's going to be very angry."

But Professor Ueno laughed when his wife told him about the shoe. "He can have those shoes," he said. "They're very old, and I only wore them in the yard."

Mrs. Ueno looked at him. "But you loved those shoes!" she said. "You need to be angry with him when he's bad, or he's never going to learn."

The next day, it was sunny, and Professor Ueno played with Hachiko after breakfast. "You must be good today," he said to the puppy. "Don't chew things – only my old shoes." And the professor put the two old shoes next to the puppy's bed. "Now I must go to work."

Later that morning, Mrs. Ueno put some clothes on the washing line in the yard. The puppy was tired, and he went to sleep in the sun.

"I'm sorry, Hachiko," Mrs. Ueno said. "I was angry with you yesterday, but you're a good puppy." She went shopping, and left Hachiko in the yard.

After Mrs. Ueno left, Hachiko opened his eyes and looked at the washing line. The clothes on the line moved in the wind, and he watched them. They moved again. How exciting! Hachiko wanted to see better so he went nearer. There was a chair under the line, and he jumped onto it, and took a white shirt in his teeth. He took a second shirt, and then a third, and soon the clothes were all over the yard! Hachiko ran and played with them.

"Oh, no!" Mrs. Ueno said angrily when she came home. "You bad dog... look at the professor's shirts!"

When Professor Ueno came home, Mrs. Ueno told her husband about the clothes. "He wants to play with everything," she said. "I can't watch him all the time."

"I'm sorry about the clothes," the professor said. "He's young and excited. But he learns fast, and I'm going to teach him. Look, he understands. He's watching you, but his ears and tail are down."

Mrs. Ueno looked at Hachiko. "Well, you must learn to be good soon, Hachiko," she said, "or you can't stay here."

"Look at the professor's shirts!"

CHAPTER THREE
Learning to Be Good

"OK, Hachiko," the professor said to the puppy the next day. "You need to be a good dog. Mrs. Ueno is going to like you, I know it, but you must learn quickly."

So the professor began teaching his puppy every day. *Stop! Sit! Go! Come! Bring it to me! No, that's not good*, the professor told the dog, and Hachiko watched, listened, and learned. The professor took him for a lot of walks in the streets near their home. Soon, Hachiko walked well with his master. He stopped and waited with him when there were bicycles or cars. And he came quickly when his master called him.

When he went past the little food stalls near Shibuya Station, he walked next to his master and never took food, so people did not get angry with him.

Often, the professor brought Hachiko to my parents' stall. He always sat quietly by the professor's feet, and I patted his head and sat with him.

"He likes you, Nobu," the professor said.

I loved it when the professor came. He was our friend, and Hachiko was our friend, too.

Spring came, and there were flowers on the cherry trees. People came out because they wanted to see the flowers, and the professor and his beautiful dog walked happily with them. Hachiko was big and strong now, and everyone liked him.

Spring came, and there were flowers on the cherry trees.

Sometimes, Professor Ueno needed to work away from Tokyo. One day, when Hachiko was only four months old, the professor was away when a typhoon – a very big storm – came to Japan.

Professor Ueno could not come home, and Mrs. Ueno was afraid. She did not like typhoons, and that night, the storm was very bad. She thought of Hachiko in his shed, in the wind and rain. At about midnight, she went and called him into the house. He came in and stayed near her, and all night, he was good, and very quiet. With Hachiko near her, Mrs. Ueno was not afraid.

"You're a good dog, Hachiko," Mrs. Ueno said.

Mrs. Ueno went and called Hachiko into the house.

CHAPTER FOUR
A Faithful Dog

Every weekday, Professor Ueno took the train to work, so in the morning he walked from his house to Shibuya Station. But before he left home, he always played with Hachiko in the yard, and then said goodbye to him. Some mornings, Mrs. Ueno came to the door and watched, and said, "Remember your train!"

"Goodbye," the professor laughed then. "Have a good day, Hachiko. Be good! Don't jump and play with the clothes on the washing line!" And he went into the street, closed the yard gate with a smile, and walked to the station.

One morning, when the professor left home, Hachiko suddenly jumped over the gate and ran down the little street. Professor Ueno heard a noise behind him, and when he looked, there was Hachiko!

"Go home, Hachiko!" the professor told the dog. "Go home now!"

But Hachiko did not want to go home, and he sat down.

"I'm going to work, Hachiko – you can't come with me," said the professor, and he began walking down the street. But the dog got up and walked behind him.

The professor laughed. "So you want to come to the station with me? All right, I understand. But then you must go home."

"Go home, Hachiko!" the professor told the dog.

Half an hour later, at the house, Mrs. Ueno looked for Hachiko. He was not in the yard, and he was not in the shed.

But then she saw Hachiko at the yard gate, on the street! He jumped over the gate and went to Mrs. Ueno with his tail up.

"Where were you?" she asked. But he looked happy, so she patted him on the head and he went to sleep in the warm sun.

The next morning, Hachiko wanted to go with the professor again.

"No, Hachiko – stay!" the professor said when he shut the gate.

But after five minutes, he heard Hachiko behind him again. The professor looked at his dog and smiled. "Go home, Hachiko!" he said kindly.

But the dog did not go home. He walked with his master to Shibuya Station, and then he came home again.

After that, Hachiko went to the station every morning – and in the evening, too! Every day at six o'clock, he jumped over the yard gate and went along the little streets to Shibuya Station. When Hachiko arrived there, he sat and waited near the ticket office. He wagged his tail happily when he saw his master, and then walked home with him.

Soon, Hachiko had many friends at the station. When people saw him there every day, they smiled. "Look at the professor's faithful dog," they said.

Hachiko wagged his tail happily when he saw his master.

The professor told us all about this when he came to our stall in the evenings. I loved to hear his stories about his special dog. One winter's day, there was a lot of snow in Tokyo. My parents did not open their stall that day. "No one is going to buy *yakitori* today," they said. But the next day, the weather was better, and that evening, Professor Ueno came and drank green tea at our stall with Hachiko.

"Hachiko is a very special dog, Nobu," the professor said to me that evening. "Yesterday morning, when I saw the snow, I said to him, 'Stay here, Hachiko! Go to your bed. It's cold today – don't come with me.'

"But Hachiko didn't want to stay – he walked to the station with me, and then went home. And yesterday evening, he walked to the station again and waited in the snow. When I arrived, his coat was white from the snow, and his paws were very cold! He came and slept in our house last night because he needed to get warm."

My father said to me later, "Professor Ueno's dog is special, Nobu, but his master is special, too. He's a good man – he's very kind to people and very kind to animals."

Professor Ueno drank green tea at our stall with Hachiko.

CHAPTER FIVE
Everything Changes

But one spring day, everything changed for Hachiko. That morning, like always, Professor Ueno walked to the station with his dog, and then patted his head, said goodbye, and went in. Hachiko walked home and jumped over the gate into the yard.

That day, the dog stayed near Mrs. Ueno when she put the clothes on the washing line in the yard; and when she went into the house, he stayed near the door. It was a warm day, and Hachiko slept. But he listened to the noises from the house, too. That day was different – and Hachiko knew it.

Again and again that morning, he barked, and when Mrs. Ueno heard him, she came into the yard. "There's nobody at the gate," she said. "Why are you barking?"

In the evening, Hachiko jumped over the gate, went to the station, and sat and waited for the professor. When the professor's usual train arrived and people walked out of the station, Hachiko stood and wagged his tail. But his master did not come. So he sat and waited again. More trains came into the station, and when they arrived, Hachiko stood and watched the people carefully. But he did not see his master. Hachiko waited and waited, and in the end, at about midnight, he walked home.

When he arrived, he jumped over the gate, went to the door of the house and barked. Mrs. Ueno slowly came out into the dark yard. She put her hand on Hachiko's warm coat for a long time. Then she began to cry, and said, "Your master isn't coming home, Hachiko. Not tonight, not tomorrow. He's never coming back."

Mrs. Ueno put her hand on Hachiko's warm coat for a long time.

She went into the house, and she called the dog. "You can sleep in the house tonight, Hachiko," she said quietly. But Hachiko looked at her and did not move. He wanted to stay in the yard, so she said, "Goodnight, Hachiko," and closed the door.

When my father told me the news about Professor Ueno, he came and sat next to me, and took my hand.

"Professor Ueno had a bad heart," he told me. "He died suddenly at the university yesterday. It's very sad. Professor Ueno was a good man."

I cried a lot that day. I cried for the kind professor, and his wife, and I cried for Hachiko. I did not go to the *yakitori* stall that evening. I stayed at home with my

mother. But when my father came home, I heard him. He told my mother, "I saw Hachiko this evening. He went to the station at five past six, and waited there for his master for hours and hours. When a train came in, he stood up and wagged his tail."

"Oh, poor Hachiko," my mother said.

"I went and saw him before I left," my father told her. "I said, 'Go home, Hachiko. He isn't coming. I'm sorry.' But he didn't go home."

Every evening after that, when we were at our stall, we saw Hachiko. He arrived at the station at five past six. He sat and waited, and when a train arrived and people came out of the station, he stood and watched.

"It's very sad," people said when they saw him.

He waited for his master for hours and hours.

CHAPTER SIX
A Sad Time

Every day that spring, Hachiko went to the station in the evening and waited for his master. One day, Mrs. Ueno came to our stall and talked to my mother.

"I feel sad in our house now, without the professor," said Mrs. Ueno. "It's a big house, too, so it's expensive. I'm going to sell it and go and live with my daughter."

"Is Hachiko going to go there with you?" my mother asked.

"No," Mrs. Ueno said. "An Akita dog needs a yard, and my daughter doesn't have a yard at her house. But my old uncle does, and he wants to help. He likes Akitas, and he would like to have Hachiko."

Three weeks later, Mrs. Ueno took Hachiko to her uncle's house. My father went and helped her. The uncle's house was two kilometers away, on a quiet Tokyo street. Mrs. Ueno and my father walked there with Hachiko, and Hachiko's new master put the dog in the yard. The yard had a high wall, and Mrs. Ueno said to my father, "Hachiko can't run to Shibuya Station from here. The wall is very high, and he doesn't know these streets."

But the next evening, Hachiko jumped over the wall, ran to Shibuya Station, and waited there. Mrs. Ueno's uncle looked for Hachiko in the streets near his house,

Hachiko's new master put the dog in the yard.

but he could not find the dog. Then the old man went to the station and saw Hachiko. He was sitting near the ticket office.

"Come on, Hachiko," Mrs. Ueno's uncle said. "The professor isn't coming. We need to go home." He took Hachiko back to his house, but every evening for two or three weeks, Hachiko jumped over the high wall and went to the station. He wanted to go and wait there for his master, Professor Ueno.

People brought him back to the uncle's yard, or the uncle went and got him – but it was no good. Hachiko did not want a new master. So Hachiko began to live in the streets near Shibuya Station.

Akitas are big dogs and they need to eat a lot of food every day, so Hachiko began coming to the back of the food stalls. Here he could sometimes find some fish or meat, or some rice – but often there was nothing for him, and some nights, Hachiko was very hungry. My parents gave him water, and sometimes some food. But they had a baby now, my sister Keiko, and they did not have a lot of money, so they could not always help Hachiko.

We always liked to see Hachiko, but not everyone was kind to him. One of the men from the food stalls did not like him, and he always chased him away. "Go away, you dirty dog!" he said, and Hachiko put his tail down and ran. Some boys liked to throw stones at Hachiko, too, when he sat near the ticket office at the station.

Some boys liked to throw stones at Hachiko.

Hachiko waited at the station for many hours every evening. He watched carefully when people walked out of the station. Some people came home through Shibuya Station every day. They wanted to go home quickly, and most of them did not look at the big dog. But some people liked to see him, and always stopped and patted his head. They knew his story from the people at the food stalls.

Late at night, Hachiko slept next to one of the buildings near the station. His big coat was warm, but on winter nights, people saw him in the cold and felt sad for him.

Hachiko slept next to one of the buildings near the station.

CHAPTER SEVEN
Famous

Years went past. When I got older, I did not see Hachiko every day. Keiko and I were at school, and in the evening we often had school work. But when I helped my father at the *yakitori* stall, I always looked for Hachiko, and took him some food when I could.

One evening, when Hachiko was by the ticket office, a man came and looked at him carefully, and talked to him. "So you are Professor Ueno's dog, Hachiko. I heard about you, and I came and watched you yesterday, and again today. It's true, you wait here every evening! You're the most faithful dog in Japan!" The man patted Hachiko's head, and Hachiko slowly wagged his tail.

Then the man went and talked to the ticket officers, and to many people in the busy little streets near the station. He asked questions and listened carefully. He took a little book out of his pocket and wrote in it.

He came to our stall, too. He told us, "My name is Mr. Saito, and I was one of Professor Ueno's students some years ago. I heard about the professor's dog, Hachiko, and I wanted to see him. He's a wonderful dog, and I want to write about him for a newspaper. I would like to tell Hachiko's story. Can I ask you some questions?"

"You're the most faithful dog in Japan!"

We talked to Mr. Saito for a long time. Three weeks later, there was a story about Hachiko in the *Asahi Shimbun*, one of the biggest newspapers in Japan. Next to the story there was a photo of Hachiko, and under the photo it said "Japan's most faithful dog."

After this, Hachiko was famous! It was exciting for everyone near Shibuya Station, and people went there every day because they wanted to see Hachiko, Japan's most faithful dog. Professor Ueno's wife lived with her old mother now, far from Tokyo, but she read the story in the newspaper, and she was happy, because she often thought about Hachiko. "He always wanted to be at the station," she said to her mother. "He wants to wait for the professor. He's a wonderful dog."

People were kinder to Hachiko now. A lot of people came and visited him, and they sometimes brought food, and stopped and patted his head. When the man from the food stall chased Hachiko away, or when the boys began to throw stones, people stopped them. "Don't do that!" they said. "Hachiko is Japan's most faithful dog. You must be kind to him."

People were kinder to Hachiko now.

❖

One day, about two years after the *Asahi Shimbun* story, my mother said to me and my sister, "Come to the stall after school today, Nobu and Keiko. There's going to be a party for Hachiko at Shibuya Station."

"A party?" we said. "Why is Hachiko having a party?"

But my mother smiled and said, "Wait and see."

When we went with our mother to the station that day, there were many people there for Hachiko's party. There were men with cameras from the newspapers, workers from the station, and many people from the Shibuya stalls. Some of Hachiko's friends from the evening trains came, and some of Professor Ueno's family were there, too.

We could not see Hachiko at first. But when we found him, we understood the party. Hachiko was sitting next to a new statue. It was a statue of a dog – a statue of Hachiko – and it was in front of the ticket office.

"Look!" said Keiko. "Now, when Hachiko comes to the station every day, he can sit and wait for his master next to the statue!"

After that wonderful party and all the different newspaper stories about him, Hachiko became more and more famous. The statue and the party brought happier times for him. He was never hungry now, and nobody threw stones at him, but he did not forget his master: he waited at the station every day.

"Hachiko can sit and wait for his master next to the statue."

Hachiko was an old dog now. When Keiko and I went and visited him at the station in the evenings, he was often asleep. Sometimes we brought nice food for him. He opened his eyes then, and stood up slowly, wagged his tail, and ate the food. But he was very old, and very tired.

One evening in 1935, our father came home early, and quietly said to my mother, Keiko, and me: "Come and sit with me. I must tell you something. I'm sorry, but Hachiko died today. I found him in a little street near the station. It's very sad."

My little sister Keiko cried then, and my mother took her hand. "He lived a long time," she told Keiko, "and he had some happy times..."

"And he was free, Keiko," I said.

My father looked at me, and he said, "You're right, Nobu. He *was* free. He wanted to wait for his master, and he did that every day. He was a very special dog. And everyone can remember him when they see his statue."

And it's true – nobody forgets Hachiko, because he was Japan's most faithful dog. He never stopped loving his master. Now, years later, when I am near Shibuya Station, I visit Hachiko's statue, and there are always many people there. Faithful friends meet at the statue and remember a very faithful dog.

Afterword

Hachiko died in March 1935, when he was eleven years old. His story is very, very famous in Japan and in many countries. In 1987, there was a Japanese film about him called *Hachiko Monogatari*, and in 2009, there was an American film with Richard Gere called *Hachi: A Dog's Tale*.

After Mr. Saito wrote about Hachiko in the *Asahi Shimbun*, a friend of Mr. Saito, called Teru Ando, made the first statue of the dog at Shibuya Station. Later, Teru Ando's son, Takeshi Ando, made a new statue – and you can see this statue at Shibuya Station today.

There are more statues of Hachiko, too. There is one in front of Odate Station, in Akita, the home of Akita dogs. And eighty years after Hachiko died, people put a wonderful statue in the gardens of the University of Tokyo. This statue is of Hachiko with Professor Ueno: the dog with his master again, after all those years.

Hachiko

GLOSSARY

baby *(n)* a very young child

bark *(v)* the noise that a dog makes

become *(v)* to begin to be something

brave *(adj)* not afraid to do dangerous or difficult things

busy *(adj)* working or not free; needing to do lots of things

chase *(v)* to run behind somebody or something because you want to get them

cherry *(n)* a small round red or black fruit

chew *(v)* to break food in your mouth with your teeth when you are eating

faithful *(adj)* A faithful person always helps their friends, and does what they say they are going to do.

farmer *(n)* a person who keeps animals and grows food

film *(n)* a story in moving pictures on television or at the cinema

fish *(n)* an animal; it lives and swims in water

food *(n)* what people and animals eat

gate *(n)* a thing like a door for a yard or field

jump *(v)* to move quickly up into the air

kind *(adj)* friendly and good to other people

master *(n)* An animal's master tells it to do or not do things.

newspaper *(n)* You read a newspaper. It is like a book with no cover, and there is news about the world/your country/your town in it.

parent *(n)* a mother or father

party *(n)* a time when friends meet, usually in somebody's home, to talk and have fun

pat *(v)* to touch somebody or something softly with your hand

paw *(n)* the foot of an animal, e.g. a dog or a cat

pay *(v)* to give somebody money for something

puppy *(n)* a young dog

rice *(n)* food that comes from a plant; we cook it and eat it

sad *(adj)* not happy

sell *(v)* to give something to somebody for money

shed *(n)* a small outside building for things or animals

snow *(n)* Snow falls from the sky when it is very cold. It turns everything white.

special *(adj)* unusual and different

stall *(n)* a big table of things to sell, e.g. in a street or market

statue *(n)* a stone or metal model of a person or animal

stone *(n)* a very hard material in the ground

stool *(n)* a small chair with no back

storm *(n)* very bad weather with lots of wind and rain

story *(n)* words by a writer about real or unreal people or things

strong *(adj)* A strong person can carry heavy things.

tail *(n)* the long, thin part at the end of an animal's body

tea *(n)* a hot drink; we make it with the leaves of a plant

throw *(v)* to move something through the air from one place to another with your arm

uncle *(n)* the brother of your mother or father, or the husband of your aunt

wag *(v)* to move a tail from side to side, or up and down

washing line *(n)* a wire or rope for drying wet clothes

wind *(n)* air that moves

yakitori *(n)* Japanese for "grilled bird" or "grilled chicken"; this is a special Japanese food, and you can eat it in food stalls and restaurants.

yard *(n)* a garden area outside a house or building, usually with a fence or wall around it

yen *(n)* Japanese money

More Faithful Dogs

Hachiko was famous because he was very, very faithful to his master. Here are two more stories about faithful dogs.

Greyfriars Bobby

Greyfriars Bobby was the dog of a man in Edinburgh, Scotland, called John Gray. John Gray was in the Edinburgh police in the 1850s. Every night, John went and worked in the cold, dark streets. Bobby lived with John for two years, and went with John when he worked. But in 1858, John died.

John's grave was at a place called Greyfriars, and after his master died, Bobby went to John's grave and stayed there. He stayed there for fourteen years. People came to the grave because they wanted to see the little dog, and he was always there, at Greyfriars. The people at a coffee shop there gave him food every day, and many people were nice to him. This faithful little dog was about sixteen years old when he died in 1872.

There is a statue of Greyfriars Bobby in Edinburgh. The statue was made in 1873. There is a film of Bobby's story, and many books about him, too.

Red Dog

In Australia, Red Dog was a famous Kelpie. Kelpies are big, strong Australian dogs with red-brown coats. Red did not have a master, and so he was free. He liked to move from town to town by bus or car. A man called John Grant was a bus driver, and he became Red's special friend. One day, sadly, John died in a road accident. Red did not understand, so he looked for John. He waited on the road for cars and buses, and when they stopped, he got in. He moved from town to town, all over Western Australia, and made lots of friends. But he had no special friend after John Grant. Red Dog lived from 1971 to 1979.

In Dampier in Western Australia, there is a statue of Red Dog. The famous writer Louis de Bernières saw this statue one day and asked people about it. He liked the story of Red Dog very much, so he wrote a book about him. There is also a film of the book. You can read this story in the *Bookworms* Stage 2 reader, *Red Dog*.

READ & RESEARCH Read "Beyond the Story" and research the answers to these questions.

1 What did Red Dog look like? Find a picture.
2 Can you find the name of another famous faithful animal? What was its name? Where did it live? Did it have a happy or difficult life?

bus *(n)* a large vehicle that carries a lot of people along the road and stops often so they can get on and off
grave *(n)* a hole in the ground where a body is buried
police *(n)* The police stop people when they break laws.

Hachiko

ACTIVITIES

Think Ahead

1 Look at the story title and cover. Work in pairs. Describe Hachiko.

2 Read the back cover. What do you think is going to happen in the story? Check (✓) the sentences you think are true.

   1 This book tells the story of a famous woman.

   2 Hachiko lived in Spain.

   3 Hachiko had a long and happy life.

   4 People remember Hachiko now.

3 **RESEARCH** Before you read, find the answers to these questions.

   1 In the story, Hachiko goes to Shibuya Station. Where is Shibuya Station? What does it look like today?

   2 Hachiko was an Akita dog. Where is Akita?

   3 When was Hachiko born? When did he die?

Chapter Check

CHAPTER 1 Choose the correct words to complete the sentences.

1 The farmer's Akita dog had *ten* / *eight* puppies.

2 The farmer's friend in Tokyo, Professor Ueno, wanted to pay *thirty yen* / *sixty yen* for a good Akita puppy.

3 Three of the puppies played in the yard and got *warm* / *cold*.

4 One of the three puppies was *braver* / *smaller* than his brothers and sisters.

5 The professor's puppy went to Tokyo by *train* / *car*.

CHAPTER 1 Complete these sentences with the correct people.

*Professor Ueno   the farmer   the farmer's children
the farmer's wife   the train driver*

1 _____ said, "They're beautiful puppies!"

2 _____ wanted to give Hachiko to Professor Ueno.

3 _____ brought the puppies in from the snow.

4 _____ took Hachiko from Akita to Tokyo.

5 _____ saw Hachiko for the first time at Shibuya Station.

CHAPTER 2 Complete the sentences with the verbs below.
There is one extra verb.

ate   came   gave   took   went   were

1 The new puppy was hungry, so he soon _____
   some rice with fish.

2 The puppy _____ to sleep in the professor's
   arms.

3 The professor and his wife _____ the dog the
   name Hachiko.

4 Hachiko _____ a white shirt in his teeth.

5 Mrs. Ueno was angry when she _____ home.

CHAPTER 2 What happened after Hachiko played with the
clothes from the washing line? Choose one answer.

1 Professor Ueno gave him some old shoes.

2 He went to live with a different family because
   Mrs. Ueno did not want him in her home.

3 Professor Ueno and his wife laughed about it.

4 Professor Ueno said, "I'm going to teach him."

CHAPTER 3 Complete the sentences with the words below.

came   learned   sat   stopped   took

1 When Professor Ueno began teaching Hachiko, he watched, listened, and _____.

2 He _____ when there were bicycles or cars.

3 When his master called him, he _____ quickly.

4 He never _____ food from the food stalls.

5 He always _____ quietly by the professor's feet at the *yakitori* stall.

CHAPTER 3 Answer the questions.

1 How old was Hachiko when the typhoon came?

2 Where was Professor Ueno?

3 Where did Hachiko stay on the night of the typhoon?

4 Why was Mrs. Ueno not afraid?

CHAPTER 4 Are the sentences true or false?

1 Every Sunday, the professor took the train to work.

2 Professor Ueno always played with Hachiko in the yard
before he left for work.

3 When it was cold, Hachiko did not wait at the station.

4 Nobu's father said to his son: "The professor is a
good man – he's very kind to people and very kind to
animals."

CHAPTER 4 Put the sentences in order.

Every day, Hachiko...

a sat and waited near the ticket office.

b walked to the station with the professor.

c and his master walked home together.

d jumped over the yard gate at six o'clock.

e wagged his tail happily when he saw his master.

f walked to Shibuya Station.

CHAPTER 5 Choose the correct words to complete the sentences.

1 One spring day was different and Hachiko *barked / ate / cried* a lot.

2 At the station that evening, Hachiko's master did not *wait / stay / come*.

3 Nobu's father told him the sad *story / book / news* about the professor.

4 Every evening after that, Nobu saw Hachiko at *home / the station / the stall*.

5 People said, "It's very *good / sad / faithful*."

CHAPTER 5 Answer the questions.

1 What time did Hachiko go home, on the night when Professor Ueno died?

2 What did he do when he arrived home?

3 Did Hachiko sleep in the house that night?

4 Where was Professor Ueno when he died?

CHAPTER 6 Who says this? Choose the correct person.

A man from the food stalls   Mrs. Ueno
Mrs. Ueno's uncle   Nobu's mother

1 "I'm going to sell our house and go and live with my daughter."

2 "Is Hachiko going to go there with you?"

3 "Come on, Hachiko. The professor isn't coming. We need to go home."

4 "Go away, you dirty dog!"

CHAPTER 6 Complete the sentences with the adjectives below.

high   hungry   kind   new   quiet

1 Mrs. Ueno's uncle lived on a _____ street.

2 The uncle's yard had a _____ wall.

3 Hachiko did not want a _____ master.

4 On some nights, Hachiko was very _____.

5 Not everyone was _____ to Hachiko.

CHAPTER 7 Put the sentences in order.

1 There was a party for Hachiko and his new statue.

2 Mr. Saito came to Shibuya Station and met Hachiko.

3 There was a story about the professor and his dog in the *Asahi Shimbun*, with a photo of Hachiko.

4 Mr. Saito asked Nobu's parents and other people some questions about Hachiko.

CHAPTER 7 Are the sentences true or false?

1 Nobu saw Hachiko every day.

2 Mr. Saito was one of Professor Ueno's students.

3 Professor Ueno's wife read about Hachiko in the newspaper.

4 Nobu and Keiko went to Hachiko's party.

5 Hachiko was often hungry before he died.

6 Hachiko stopped waiting at the station after the party.

AFTERWORD Answer the questions.

1 How old was Hachiko when he died?

2 Who made the first statue of Hachiko?

3 Where was this statue?

Focus on Vocabulary

1 Complete the sentences with the correct verbs.

becomes   jump   sell   wash

1 When something is dirty, you _____ it.

2 A dog can _____ to get over a wall.

3 People _____ things in shops or from a stall.

4 When a puppy gets older, it _____ a dog.

2 Complete the sentences with food and drink words.

1 Puppies drink their mother's _____.

2 When Professor Ueno took his new puppy home, he gave him _____ and _____.

3 Nobu's parents had a *yakitori* stall. *Yakitori* is made with _____.

4 Mr. Saito sometimes had _____ at their stall.

3 Match.

1 A young dog.   a Bark.

2 You do this when you like a dog.   b A puppy.

3 A dog does this when it is happy.   c Paws.

4 A dog has four of these.   d It wags its tail.

5 A dog cannot speak, but it can   e You pat it.
  do this.

Focus on Language

1 Choose the correct verb and put it into the past simple.

~~be~~   be   become   die   go   live   want

Hachiko _____was_____ an Akita dog. He _____
near Shibuya Station in Tokyo with his master. He
_____ very famous because he _____ very
faithful. After his master _____, he _____
to the station every day. He _____ to wait for his
master here.

2 **DECODE** Read this text from the story and underline all
the personal pronouns (*I/me, he/him, we/us,* etc.).

Professor Ueno worked at the University of Tokyo, and the
next day, when he went to work, Hachiko stayed at home
in the yard. He played there happily. Then he found a shoe
near the front door of the house, and he took it to his bed
and chewed it.

"Stop, and give me that shoe," Mrs. Ueno said when
she came into the yard. "You bad dog! That's one of the
professor's shoes! He's going to be very angry."

But Professor Ueno laughed when his wife told him
about the shoe. "He can have those shoes," he said.
"They're very old, and I only wore them in the yard."

3 Who does each personal pronoun stand for in exercise 2?
For example, the first *he* stands for *Professor Ueno*.

Discussion

1 Read the discussion between three friends. Do you agree with Gina and Kenzo, or do you agree with Tori?

GINA: I think that sad stories are good, because you never forget them.

KENZO: I do, too. With sad stories, you think about them all the time.

TORI: I don't. I think that you need to read happy things. I don't want to feel sad when I read a story.

2 Look at the discussion in exercise 1. Find one word or phrase for...

• giving an opinion
• giving reasons for your opinion
• agreeing
• disagreeing

3 **THINK CRITICALLY** Read the sentence below. Do you agree with it or disagree? List three or more reasons for your opinion.

A dog is good for a family.

4 **COMMUNICATE** Now find a partner who disagrees with you. Discuss the sentence in exercise 3, using the words and phrases from exercise 2.

1 **Read the profiles below and complete this text about the differences between Akita dogs and Kelpie dogs.**

Akitas are from _____, but Kelpies are from _____. Akitas are usually red, white, or brown, and Kelpies are usually _____. _____ are heavier than _____, and they are taller, too. Akitas usually live for _____, and Kelpies live for _____. Akitas are loving and _____, and Kelpies are _____ and _____.

AKITA DOGS
From: Japan
Color: red, white, brown
Weight: about 50 kg
Height: about 60 cm
Live for: 10–15 years
Personality: loving, faithful

KELPIE DOGS	
From: Australia	
Color: black, brown, red	
Weight: about 29 kg	
Height: about 45 cm	
Live for: 10–13 years	
Personality: friendly, clever	

2 **CREATE** Now find out more information about another type of dog and write a profile for it like the ones above.

3 **COLLABORATE** Work in pairs. Read your partner's profile and talk about the differences between the kinds of dog you chose.

If you liked this Bookworm, why not try...

The Elephant Man

STAGE 1
Tim Vicary

He is not beautiful. His mother does not want him, children run away from him. People laugh at him, and call him 'The Elephant Man'.

Then someone speaks to him – and listens to him! At the age of 27, Joseph Merrick finds a friend for the first time in his life. This is a true and tragic story.

Red Dog

STAGE 2
Louis de Bernières

Red Dog was a Red Cloud kelpie, an Australian sheepdog. His life was full of excitement and adventure. He travelled all over Western Australia, and never really had an owner. Louis de Bernières collected these stories about the life of a real dog in Australia.
